Contents

Edition 2.3

© 2019. Qualsafe Limited. All Rights Reserved.

No part of this publication may be reproduced, stored in a retrieval system, or transmitted in form or by any means, electronic, mechanical, photocopying, recording or otherwise, without the prior written permission of the copyright owner.
Tel: 0845 644 3305   www.qualsafe.com

This book is designed as a learning guide for Level 2 Health and Safety courses and is not intended as an authoritative guide to Health and Safety law. Whilst every effort has been made to ensure the accuracy of the information contained within this book, the publisher does not accept liability for any loss that may be caused as a result of any inaccurate information identified within this book.

The Essence of Health and Safety

Every year, accidents at work cost UK industry billions of pounds. The effects of the injuries sustained vary from needing an extended period of time off work, never being able to work again, to the injuries being fatal. The sad fact is, many of these accidents need not have happened.

Much of health and safety is common sense. If individuals are aware of potential hazards and adopt safe working practices, they can control the risks and reduce the number of accidents and injuries.

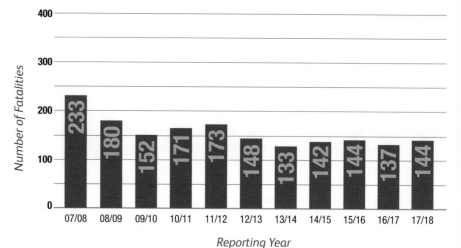

Number of fatal injuries to employees

Source: Health and Safety Executive

Don't Become a Statistic

In 2017/2018

Fact!

144 workers were killed at work and 71,062 workplace injuries were reported under RIDDOR.

Fact!

30.7 million working days were lost due to **work-related illness** and **workplace injury**.

Fact!

1.4 million working people suffer from a work-related illness.

Fact!

Workplace injuries and ill health cost society an estimated **£15 billion**.

Fact!

2,595 people died due to **mesothelioma** in 2016 and thousands more from other work-related cancers and diseases such as COPD.

Source: Health & Safety Executive statistics for 2017/18

Common causes of accidents in the workplace are:

- Slips, trips and falls
- Poor lifting and carrying
- Being struck by vehicles or moving objects
- Falls from height
- Misuse of machinery
- Incorrect use of harmful substances

Work related activities can also be responsible for diseases and ill health – in some cases with long term, irreversible effects. Examples include:

- Hearing loss from noisy workplaces
- Stress
- Skin disorders
- Hand Arm Vibration Syndrome *(HAVS)*
- Back pain
- Asbestosis and cancer as a result of asbestos exposure
- Work-related lung diseases and cancers

These hazards can be controlled by assessing risks and putting in effective controls.

Good health and safety standards will not only minimise the pain and personal consequences to individual employees, but also reduce the financial impact on employers and services funded by the taxpayer.

Health and Safety in the Press

The Times

Worker killed by forklift

A Livingston firm has been fined £100,000 after a worker was killed when he was hit by a forklift truck so badly loaded its driver could not see him.

George Hardie, 60, from Livingston, was walking across the yard at Vion Food Scotland Ltd in Broxburn, West Lothian, on 2 June 2009 to drop paperwork off at another part of the site.

As he was walking, a colleague was driving a forklift carrying two large empty containers across the yard to be washed.

The containers were stacked on top of each other on the front of the forklift, and the top of the load was approximately 160cm from the ground, making it hard for the driver to see over them.

As the driver approached the container wash, he felt his truck go over something, stopped, climbed out and saw Mr Hardie lying on his back, with the lower half of his body trapped underneath the forklift.

Colleagues attempted to help Mr Hardie before the emergency services arrived. Fire crews freed Mr Hardie, but when paramedics treated him they found he was not breathing and there were no signs of life. He was taken to the New Edinburgh Royal Infirmary, but was found to be dead on arrival.

The Times

Pork producer fined after worker severs fingers

The UK's biggest producer of pork products has been fined after a worker severed two fingers in an unguarded mixing machine. The incident happened as he reached into the mixing bowl to remove a piece of blue plastic that he had spotted as he was adding seasoning to the mixture.

A Health and Safety Executive (HSE) investigation found the mixing machine was not guarded, unlike others at the site which all had an electrically locked gate at the top of a set of access steps. If gates had been in place, they would have prevented the paddles inside the machine from turning as the seasoning was added.

The Times

Company fined after man dies from fall

A Barnet-based wholesaler has been fined after a man died of injuries sustained when he fell from a stepladder. The Health and Safety Executive (HSE) prosecuted Ovenpride Wholesale Ltd and manager Amjad Mahmood for failing to provide a safe system of work which, led to the death of a handyman. He was employed as a casual handyman at Ovenpride's Finchley Rd Bakery and was asked to build shelving in the storeroom by the site manager. During the morning Mr Carofalo had been seen standing on a stepladder while working on the shelving using tools and materials provided by Ovenpride. At around midday he was found lying on the floor bleeding from a severe head wound, with the stepladder beside him. He died as a result of his injuries.

"Where access to heights is required, even for relatively short term work, they are ultimately responsible for assessing and planning the work and ensuring that it is carried out in a safe manner using suitable access equipment."

The Times

Brewery fined after three men burned by caustic soda

A Burton-on-Trent brewery has been fined after three men suffered serious chemical burns when 6,000 litres of caustic soda erupted from a faulty valve.

The three sub-contractors were drenched in a liquid jet of caustic soda when repairing a valve on a line running from a detergent tank. Up to 6,000 litres of the chemical spilled out from the container.

Cannock Magistrates' Court heard the men had not been given adequate instructions or appropriate personal protective equipment. Although they were given visors, the overalls provided by the company were made from cloth, and the caustic fluid soaked through these. "This was a preventable incident, which caused unpleasant injuries to three men. It is fortunate that the caustic soda was dilute, otherwise they would have been much more seriously hurt. All companies must manage contractors properly and make sure that they are following health and safety procedures. They must also carry out proper risk assessments for any work that contractors are required to carry out. Molson Coors failed to do this, and three people have been injured as a result."

Business costs

- Legal advice and insurance costs
- Legal action, possibly including compensation
- Sick pay
- Lost production and sales
- Equipment and stock losses and damage
- Time and money spent on investigations and improvements
- Recruitment and payment of cover/replacement staff

But these can fade into insignificance when weighed against the human costs.

Human costs

- Pain and suffering
- Disability, possibly long-term
- Health care and rehabilitation
- Loss of earnings
- Emotional and financial burden on family
- Potential loss of life

Health and Safety Law

The Health and Safety at Work etc. Act came into force in 1974 and covers everyone at work *(apart from persons attending domestic premises)*. The Act makes it clear that everyone has a part to play in health and safety at work. The main purpose is to encourage high standards and prevent people coming to harm at work. The responsibilities of various parties under the Act are detailed below:

Employers

The Act places a 'duty of care' on employers to introduce good health and safety practices and provides a framework for health and safety regulations. They must ensure the health, safety and welfare of employees, visitors and the public by providing:

- A written Health and Safety Policy *(if they employ 5 or more people)*
- Safe equipment and machinery
- Safe systems of work
- Information, instruction, supervision and training
- Safe working environment
- Adequate welfare facilities

Employees

Under the Health and Safety at Work etc. Act all employees have a duty to:

- Act in a way that does not put themselves or others at risk
- Co-operate with their employer on any health and safety matters

Self-Employed

Health and safety law does not apply to people who are self-employed if their work activity does not cause any potential risks to the health and safety of others, e.g. accountants, novelists.

However, health and safety law will apply to the self-employed if:

- They employ other people
- Their work presents a potential risk to the health and safety of others
- Their work activity is specifically mentioned in the Health and Safety at Work etc. Act 1974 *(General Duties of Self-Employed Persons) (Prescribed Undertakings)* Regulations 2015

When relevant, self-employed people share many of the same duties as employers. They must make sure their work does not endanger themselves or others and inform people of hazards, e.g. by putting up signs to alert others to hazards.

Occupiers of Buildings

Persons in control of buildings have duties to people who are not employed by them but work at or visit the premises, e.g. customers, contractors, visitors, etc.

Designers, Manufacturers and Installers

Equipment and articles must be designed, constructed and tested to make sure they work safely and any substances used in their manufacture must be safe. Adequate information on the safe use of the equipment must be provided.

> You are responsible not only for your own health and safety, but also for the health and safety of others in the workplace.

Health and safety policy statement
Health and Safety at Work etc. Act 1974

This is the Health and Safety Policy Statement of

Health and safety policy

Where five or more people are employed, the law requires a written health and safety policy. This policy should be kept as simple as possible but should include the following:

A statement of intent – a general statement outlining how the company intends to ensure a safe working environment.

Organisation details – the individuals with specific responsibilities and the lines of accountability.

Working arrangements – the working procedures to ensure all work is conducted safely. It is important this information is communicated to all employees. The policy will only be effective if it is regularly reviewed and everyone follows it.

Specific Regulations

Although the Health and Safety at Work etc. Act (1974) covers the workplace and those affected by the work undertaken, some activities have additional specific legislation:

- Work areas
- Equipment
- Signs
- Electricity
- Fire
- Chemicals
- Noise
- Computers and display screen equipment
- Manual handling
- Personal Protective Equipment (PPE)
- Accident reporting
- Asbestos
- Vibration
- Working at height

The Management of Health and Safety at Work Regulations *(1999)* require employers to identify and assess risks in their workplace. The findings of the risk assessment must be recorded if five or more people are employed. 'Competent people' must be appointed to undertake the assessment and implement any safety measures identified as necessary. A competent person is someone who has sufficient training, experience or knowledge to enable them to properly assist the employer in complying with health and safety legislation.

The regulations also require employers to:

- Set up emergency procedures
- Provide clear information and training to employees
- Share information on risks and co-ordinate control measures with other employers that use the same workplace
- Regularly review risks and safety measures – where appropriate these should be updated to reflect any changes

Penalties and Enforcement

The Health and Safety at Work etc. Act (1974) is enforced by Health and Safety Executive Inspectors and Local Authority Environmental Health Officers *(EHO)*. Their powers are far reaching and include the right to enter premises, dismantle equipment, take samples, seize articles and stop people working if there is imminent danger. The main function of the inspectors and EHOs is to offer information and guidance to employers to improve health and safety awareness and make workplaces safer. In cases where informal advice has not been followed or they feel there is an unacceptable level of risk, the following types of legal notice can be served:

An Improvement Notice – This type of notice will state what is wrong, what should be done about it and the time allowed for changes to be made.

A Prohibition Notice – If there is an immediate danger to individuals, this notice can prevent an unsafe activity being carried out or can stop all or part of a workplace being used.

> Failure to comply with a notice is a criminal offence. Substantial fines can be issued and in severe cases, the courts can imprison those found guilty for up to 2 years.

Civil Law

In addition to being prosecuted for breaking the law of the land *(criminal law)*, civil law allows private parties to claim compensation for injuries/damages against others that have caused them loss or suffering.

Fee For Intervention (FFI)

Under the Health and Safety (Fees) Regulations 2012, those found to have broken health and safety law will be charged a fee for the amount it has cost the Health and Safety Executive to investigate and take enforcement action.

The courts can imprison those found guilty for up to 2 years.

Accidents and their Prevention

While accidents are defined as unplanned or uncontrolled events, the truth is that many accidents can be avoided. An accident is an incident that may cause:

- Major or serious personal injuries or damage to the workplace
- Minor damage or injuries
- A near miss
- Death

Being aware of the existence of hazards and the control of risks is essential for accident prevention. There are three factors that cause problems in the workplace:

Occupational – Injury or illness directly connected to work related tasks such as lifting and carrying or using tools and equipment.

Environmental – Conditions in the workplace such as heating, ventilation, lighting and space that can affect the safety of workers.

Human – Lack of training, inexperience, complacency, disregard for safety rules, haste, distraction and tiredness are examples of human factors that can contribute to accidents. Unfortunately many human hazards are very difficult to control.

Bird's research shows that for every one accident causing a major injury, there are 30 minor injuries and 300 incidents where there were no injuries. **Therefore it is vital that every accident, regardless of injury, is reported and investigated.**

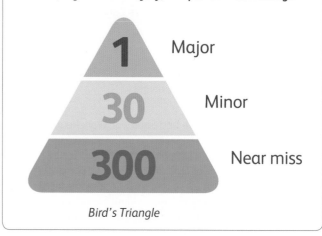

Bird's Triangle

Examples of the causes of accidents

Kitchen worker removes palm of their hand with a meat slicer

Possible causes:

- The operative was using an unsafe work practice
- No training had been given
- No guard in place – it could have been removed to obtain more sliced product
- Haste to get job done

Employee cut by broken glass in bin

Possible causes:

- Broken glass not correctly wrapped up
- Employee pushing glass deep into bin
- Employee compacting rubbish without Personal Protective Equipment (PPE)

Visitor falls down storeroom steps

Possible causes:

- Bad design where visitors have access to storeroom
- Obstruction left at top of steps
- Storeroom door next to toilet door
- Door had been left unlocked
- Visitor mistook the doors because of poor signage
- No warning of steps

It soon becomes apparent that many causes may contribute to an accident occurring.

Possible causes of accidents:

- Poor building structure and design
- Equipment poorly designed, selected, constructed, guarded or maintained
- Poor housekeeping such as obstructions in passageways

- Poor lighting
- Poor ventilation
- Lack of training and information
- Bad work practices
- Distraction
- Practical jokes and horseplay

- Use of alcohol and drugs
- Illness and fatigue
- Haste
- Ignoring safety rules and measures
- Clothing

There may also be some general issues affecting safety such as stress, smoking and the threat of, or actual violence. *(See page 17 – Occupational Health).*

Investigating and Analysing

It is vital that managers create a positive attitude to health and safety matters and make sure all members of the team take health and safety seriously. Everyone in the workplace **must** follow procedures and report defects.

Employers need to be made aware of occurrences so they can be prevented from happening again. All accidents, including near misses and all incidents of ill-health should be reported, their cause investigated and corrective action taken. Employees have a duty to report occurrences to their employer.

Accidents and incidents can be reported in the form of an Accident Book, which should contain the following information:

- Date and time of injury
- Name of the injured person
- A description of the accident and nature of the injury
- What action was taken and by whom
- Final outcome, e.g. employee sent home, hospitalised, etc.
- Person reporting the injury *(if it is not the injured person)*

RIDDOR

RIDDOR *(Reporting of Injuries, Diseases and Dangerous Occurrences Regulations 2013)* requires employers *(including self-employed)* or those in control of premises to report the following occurrences directly to the HSE:

Incident/occurrence	Must be reported to HSE:
Death Any work-related fatality.	Immediately
Specified injuries e.g. amputation, loss of sight and most fractures.	Immediately
Occupational diseases When a disease is likely to have been caused or made worse due to the nature of a person's work, e.g. occupational dermatitis, tendonitis. A full list of reportable diseases is available from the RIDDOR website.	As soon as a diagnosis from a doctor has been received by the responsible person
Dangerous occurrences Near-misses that do not result in an injury but could have, e.g. collapse of scaffolding or accidental release of a dangerous substance.	Immediately
Injuries to members of the public When an incident has caused death or an injury requiring hospital treatment to a person who is not at work.	Immediately
Gas incidents Importers and suppliers of gas must report death or injuries related to that gas. Gas Safe registered engineers must report details of any gas fittings or appliances that could cause serious danger to the public.	Immediately
Over 7 day injuries Where an employee or self-employed person is away from work or unable to perform their normal duties for more than 7 consecutive days.	Within 15 days

By law, employers must also keep a record of all injuries that result in workers being unable to work for more than 3 consecutive days *(an Accident Book entry is acceptable)*. It is always good practice, and in some cases a legal requirement, to record all accidents and near-misses.

More detailed information on what should be reported can be found on the HSE website: **www.hse.gov.uk/riddor**

All incidents and occurrences can be reported using the website and a telephone service remains for reporting fatal and major injuries: **0345 300 9923**.

Controlling risks and positive attitudes help prevent accidents.

Risk Assessment

The Management of Health and Safety at Work Regulations 1999 requires the employer to arrange for competent person(s) to carry out a detailed risk assessment. It should identify all workplace hazards, quantify the risks and introduce control measures to reduce the risk of injury or illness to the workforce. If more than five persons are employed, the assessment must be recorded.

Other legislation also requires employers to conduct specific risk assessments for specific hazards e.g. manual handling, hazardous substances, display screen equipment and fire.

A risk assessment is simply a careful examination of what could cause harm to people so you can consider whether you have taken enough precautions or should do more to prevent harm.

Risk assessments will help identify what could go wrong, how likely it is to happen and how serious the result could be. The employer then needs to put control measures in place to prevent the problem occurring.

Hazard and risk have two quite distinct meanings:

HAZARD: Something that has the potential to cause harm or damage.

RISK: The likelihood of the harm or damage being realised.

For example: A bottle of bleach contains a hazard, but locked in the cupboard it does little harm. The risk increases when the bottle is used.

Five Steps of a Risk Assessment

1

Identify the hazards – Examples include:

Slips and trips – consider floor surfaces, housekeeping and different floor levels.

Working at height – e.g. decorators using ladders and construction workers on scaffolding.

Fire hazards – e.g. flammable substances and sources of ignition.

Moving vehicles – e.g. forklift trucks and reversing lorries.

Dust – such as wood dust in a sawmill or flour in a bakery.

Hot liquids – e.g. pans of hot water or oil in a kitchen.

2

Decide on who may be harmed and how

It is not just the person conducting the task that may be affected but anyone nearby. For example, builders working on scaffolding above a public walkway may injure pedestrians if equipment or materials are dropped.

Some employees will need a separate risk assessment, e.g. those who are more vulnerable, such as pregnant workers and young, inexperienced staff.

3

Evaluate the risk and decide on precautions

Consider the consequences of injury or harm. Could someone be seriously injured or killed? Could lots of people be affected? Is it likely to occur? If the answer is yes then these hazards should be addressed as a priority and further controls put in place to reduce the risk to an acceptable level, using the hierarchy of control *(see page 9)*.

4

Record your significant findings and implement them

It is a legal requirement that businesses with 5 or more staff formally record their significant findings. It is important not only to implement the controls you identified, making sure staff are trained in the new procedures, but to check to make sure they are being followed correctly.

5

Review and update risk assessments

Reviews should take place when:

- Procedures are revised
- Workplace layout is reorganised
- New machinery is installed
- An accident or near miss occurs
- The law changes

Reviews should also take place on a regular basis, possibly annually, just to make sure nothing has been missed and to identify new techniques or scientific developments that could be introduced to improve safety.

Hierarchy of Control

When considering control measures there is a scale of preference *(listed below)*. The higher up the chart, the better or more preferable the method. Some measures will work for some tasks or activities and some for others, but not all will be suitable.

1 **Eliminate:**
If something is hazardous the most effective option is to remove it.

2 **Substitute:**
Can something safer be substituted for it?

3 **Engineering controls:**
Examples include:

Equipment – using work equipment as a preventative measure, e.g. to prevent falls from height.

Guards – placing or replacing guarding controls.

Insulation – an excellent method of noise control.

Isolation – separating the worker from the hazard.

Ventilation – removing hazardous dust and fumes from the workplace using additional machinery if necessary.

Maintenance – making sure all equipment is well serviced and maintained.

4 **Administrative controls:**
Procedures needed to work safely, e.g. limiting the amount of time the worker is exposed to a hazard, increasing safety signage, conducting risk assessments.

5 **Personal Protective Equipment (PPE):**
Equipment or clothing provided to protect an employee against risks to their health and safety *(see page 24–25)*. Must only be used once all other measures have been tried and found unsuitable.

Competent person

A person who has sufficient training, experience, knowledge or other relevant qualities to enable them to undertake a task or job.

Risk assessments are used to look for possible causes of accidents and to assess how bad the results may be.

Fire Safety

The Regulatory Reform *(Fire Safety)* Order 2005 replaced more than seventy separate laws on fire legislation in England and Wales *(similar legislation was also introduced in Scotland and Northern Ireland)*. Under this law, a 'responsible person' is someone who has control over all or part of a workplace *(this is usually the employer, building owner or occupier)*. The 'responsible person' must carry out a Fire Safety Risk Assessment *(FSRA)* and make sure appropriate fire prevention and protection measures are in place to minimise the risks from fire. This will include ensuring fire safety equipment is operational and maintained, providing appropriate training, preparing an emergency plan and reviewing the FSRA findings regularly to reflect any changes.

All employees have a legal duty to co-operate with their employer on fire safety matters.

Causes of Workplace Fires

- Smoking
- Arson
- Electrical equipment and wiring *(faulty, poorly maintained or misused)*
- Portable heaters
- Cooking
- Poor housekeeping/accumulated rubbish
- Hot working practices *(such as soldering or welding)*

Fire Hazards

A hazard is anything that may cause harm. The table below shows examples of fire hazards and some of their possible effects:

Hazards	Potential to cause harm
Flames and heat	Breathing superheated air can be an instant killer due to the damage caused to the airway and lungs. Burns covering over 20 % of the body are usually regarded as life-threatening. Burns to the eyes can result in blindness.
Smoke and fumes	Inhalation of smoke is the most common cause of death in fires. A build-up of carbon monoxide can put people into a deeper 'sleep'. Fumes from plastics and man-made fibres can kill – for this reason fire retardant materials are now a requirement in new furniture.
Lack of oxygen	Fire uses up oxygen from the atmosphere. If the brain is starved of oxygen this can quickly lead to unconsciousness and death.
Impact and crushing	Fire damage may weaken a building to the point where it starts to collapse. Crush injuries, fractures and head injuries are all possible.
No escape route	Locked doors or blocked routes can prevent safe escape in a fire. The presence of fire itself may block an escape route.

The Fire Triangle

Fire needs three things to develop – take away one of these and the fire will die out.

Heat

A fire cannot begin without an ignition source – take away the heat and there will be nothing to start the fire. Sources of ignition include:

- Naked flames
- Gas fires
- Electrical equipment
- Heaters
- Smoking
- Sparks

Oxygen

Fire needs oxygen to burn. This is generally in the atmosphere around us, but can be supplemented by bottled oxygen, depending on the type of business. This is why fire wardens close doors and windows when doing a sweep of their area in a fire situation, to cut off the supply of oxygen and starve the fire.

Fuel

As most things can burn, virtually anything can be a fuel. Commonly found sources of combustible fuels include:

- Textiles
- Cardboard
- Rubbish
- Paper
- Wood
- Gases
- Plastics

Fire Prevention *(stopping fires occurring)*

In most cases, fire prevention involves simple measures that can be undertaken using the knowledge of how fires develop. Fire prevention at its most basic is based on the principle of keeping fuel sources and ignition sources separate – keep things that burn away from things that create heat.

ALWAYS	NEVER
✔ Be aware: Identify fire hazards and minimise the risk	✘ Overload electrical sockets
✔ Remove rubbish and waste products from the premises regularly	✘ Block air vents on equipment
✔ Take care with flammable materials and liquids	✘ Put out cigarettes in waste paper bins
✔ Unplug non-essential equipment when it is not in use	✘ Put anything on top of a heater
✔ Smoke in designated areas outside the workplace only	

Actions on Discovering a Fire

If you discover a fire *(or even suspect there may be one)* you should:

- Raise the alarm
- Make sure the fire service is called
- Evacuate the building following the procedures of your workplace

Actions on Hearing the Alarm

Each workplace should have its own procedures for what to do in the event of a fire. The table below contains some simple advice on what you should and shouldn't do when the alarm is raised:

ALWAYS	NEVER
✔ Stay calm and act immediately	✘ Delay your evacuation by collecting your belongings, finishing a task or waiting for others to react
✔ Leave the building by the nearest exit	✘ Use lifts *(unless this is part of a personal emergency evacuation plan)*
✔ Close windows and doors behind you *(if you are the last to leave)*	✘ Tackle a fire unless you are trained and it is safe to do so
✔ Assemble at your designated assembly point and wait to be accounted for	✘ Re-enter the building until you are told it is safe

Evacuation Procedures

It is essential for all companies to have an evacuation procedure. In the event of a fire everyone must be able to leave the building with the least trouble and panic in the shortest possible time. To facilitate this, fire training and practice must be held regularly and fire duties assigned. Regular practice can save lives and avoid excess damage.

Fire Doors, Exits and Escapes

Internal fire doors with self-closing devices play a vital part in preventing fire spread, so it is important not to wedge them open *(especially with fire extinguishers)*. Some fire doors are designed to be held open by magnets. To make sure they will close automatically in the event of a fire, they need to be kept free from any obstructions and tested regularly.

All internal fire doors should be labelled. These signs are white squares with a blue inner circle stating it is a fire door and should be kept shut. A good fire door could hold a fire back for thirty minutes, enabling everyone to get to safety.

All escape routes should eventually lead to a fire exit that should open outwards. This can be an exit that is used only in an emergency or a normal entrance to the building that is used regularly. Fire exits can be locked at night for added security but they must be unlocked as soon as anyone is in the building.

Fire exits must be signed from inside the building and should be checked regularly to make sure they fully open and close properly. Any obstruction on the outside of a fire door could prevent it from opening in an emergency. 'Fire exit, keep clear' signs should be used and the floor marked with a yellow-hatched box where the door opens to reduce the likelihood of this happening.

Fire Extinguishers

Fire extinguishers are red with a coloured label to indicate its type. A sign giving details of its type and use must be placed by the extinguisher.

RED LABEL	CREAM LABEL	BLUE LABEL	BLACK LABEL	YELLOW LABEL
Water	Foam	Powder	Carbon Dioxide	Wet Chemical
Only suitable for use on solid materials such as wood, paper, straw, textiles, coal, etc. Some water extinguishers contain additives to make them more effective. Do not use on electrical equipment, cooking oil, fat pan fires or flammable metal fires.	Can be used on flammable liquids *(e.g. paint, petrol, diesel, etc.)* or on solid materials *(e.g. wood, paper, straw, etc.)*. Do not use on electrical equipment *(unless stated otherwise)* or cooking oil, fat pan fires or flammable metal fires.	Can be used on most types of fire *(but it could damage electrical equipment)*. Not suitable for confined places *(can affect visibility and people with breathing problems)*. Do not use on cooking oil, fat pan fires or flammable metal fires.	Suitable for fires involving electrical equipment *(even when live)*. Can also be used on flammable liquids. Fire can re-ignite as it does not cool very well. The discharge horn and hose may freeze and could cause cold burns if in direct contact with skin.	The only extinguisher that can be used on cooking oils and fats *(e.g. lard, butter, olive oil, sunflower oil, etc.)* Should not be used on petrol, spirits or mineral oils. Check manufacturer's instructions for other uses.

Extinguishing Fires

To extinguish a fire, one or more of the elements in the fire triangle has to be removed or reduced to a level where it will no longer support combustion.

Most extinguishers work by smothering or cooling the fire *(or a combination of both methods)*.

Employers and those responsible for premises must provide appropriate firefighting equipment and make sure sufficient people are trained in its use.

You should only attempt to fight a fire if it is safe to do so!

Starving *(reducing the fuel)*

Cooling *(reducing the heat)*

HEAT
FUEL
OXYGEN

Smothering
(reducing the oxygen)

You should only ever attempt to fight a fire if:

- Someone has raised the alarm
- The emergency services have been called
- The correct type of extinguisher is available
- You are competent and have been trained to use the extinguisher
- A safe escape route is available
- The fire is smaller than a waste paper bin

Do not fight a fire if:

- The room is filling with smoke or the fire is spreading
- Other hazards are present *(such as chemicals or gas cylinders)*
- The fire is not reducing or more than one extinguisher is required

Whilst different extinguishers should have their instructions for use on the cylinder, the general advice for operating a fire extinguisher can be remembered as **PASS**.

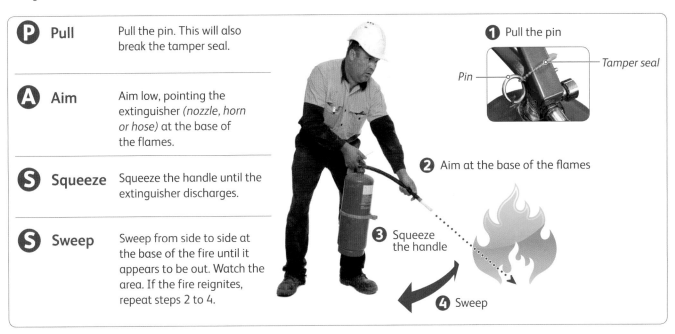

P Pull	Pull the pin. This will also break the tamper seal.
A Aim	Aim low, pointing the extinguisher *(nozzle, horn or hose)* at the base of the flames.
S Squeeze	Squeeze the handle until the extinguisher discharges.
S Sweep	Sweep from side to side at the base of the fire until it appears to be out. Watch the area. If the fire reignites, repeat steps 2 to 4.

❶ Pull the pin
Tamper seal
Pin

❷ Aim at the base of the flames

❸ Squeeze the handle

❹ Sweep

Regular evacuation practice can save lives and avoid excess damage.

⚠ Remove one element of the fire triangle and there can be no fire.

Electricity

Most people use some form of electrical equipment every day. It is this familiarity that leads to carelessness with electricity and a disregard for the risks. Examples include: overloading electricity outlets, working on electrical equipment while it is still connected to the power supply, using plugs fitted with the wrong fuse and even using equipment that does not have a fused plug fitted.

Electricity can affect the worker in a number of ways:

Burns

Electricity invariably burns *(both entry and exit burns)* and serious injuries can take a long time to heal.

Flash

Electrical flashes are extremely bright and can burn or damage the eyes.

Shocks

Electricity passing through the body can affect the heart and kill instantly.

Fires

20% of accidental fires in the workplace are caused by electrical faults.

Electricity can affect the heart's electrical impulses and kill instantly.

Using Electrical Equipment Safely

ALWAYS	NEVER
✔ Check the equipment before use	✘ Handle the plug with wet hands
✔ Switch it off before unplugging the machine	✘ Use electrical equipment in wet conditions
✔ Report all faults immediately and remove the equipment from use so no-one else can use it and get injured	✘ Use electrical equipment unless you have been trained in its use
	✘ Overload electrical sockets
✔ Turn off the power when servicing electrical equipment	✘ Overload extension leads *(don't plug in a combination of appliances that will exceed the maximum current rating for the lead)*
	✘ Attempt repairs unless qualified to do so

Electrical Equipment Checks

Electrical cables, flexes, tools and equipment should be regularly checked and faults reported. Portable appliances should be checked periodically *(usually annually)* by a competent person.

A high percentage of faults with electrical equipment can be found by just looking at it. Everyone can play a role in improving safety by making quick visual checks of the equipment they use.

Things to look for:

- Damage to cables, e.g. cuts and abrasions to the cable covering
- Damage to plugs, e.g. cracked casing or broken pins
- Loose cables, e.g. the outer covering of the cable not being gripped properly by the plug
- Signs of overheating, e.g. burn marks, staining or melted plastic
- Bare wires *(none should be visible)*
- Coiled extension cables *(make sure coiled extension cables are fully extended when in use)*

If you notice any of the faults listed, a qualified person should undertake any necessary repairs.

Make sure all plugs are correctly fitted with the correct rating of fuse and all the wires are securely gripped in the correct place.

Dealing with Electric Shock

A shock occurs when an electrical current passes through the body. This can interfere with the body's own electrical impulses and may cause the heart or breathing to stop. Burns may be seen where the current enters and exits the body. There may also be deep internal damage which cannot be seen along the path of the current.

In the event of someone suffering an electric shock:

- **Seek help and do not put yourself at risk**
- Make sure the contact with the electricity is broken before you touch the casualty. Turn off the power at the mains or unplug the appliance if possible. Do not touch anything that is metal or wet
- For high voltage supplies *(such as overhead power lines)* do not allow anyone within 18 metres of the casualty
- Once the power is disconnected safely, someone with first aid knowledge can give first aid. This may involve giving CPR or treating any burns or injuries
- Take the casualty to hospital for a check-up *(even if they have apparently recovered)*. **Call 999/112** for emergency help if the casualty has been unconscious or has electrical burns

For your Protection:

Electricity is an essential part of our daily lives and it is easy to forget that it is dangerous. There are a number of ways electrical risk can be reduced:

Insulation – to protect the user from contact.

Earthing – to provide a contact with earth reducing the risk of shock.

Fuses – strips of metal *(usually inside a cartridge)* which melt if exposed to excessive current or electrical fault, thus breaking the supply.

Circuit breakers – detect excess electric current and stop the supply *(as with fuses they must be correctly rated)*.

Residual Current Devices (RCD) – electronic device to shut off power in the event of a fault.

Voltage reduction – using a lower voltage.

UK Plugs – What fuse to use:

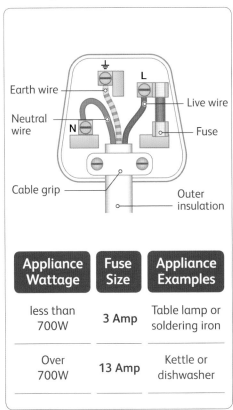

Appliance Wattage	Fuse Size	Appliance Examples
less than 700W	3 Amp	Table lamp or soldering iron
Over 700W	13 Amp	Kettle or dishwasher

4 spaces doesn't always mean 4 plugs!

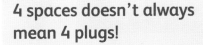

| 3 | + | 5 | + | 5 | = | 13 |
| Amp | | Amp | | Amp | | Amp |

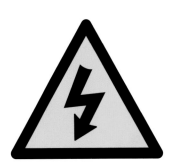

Every electric shock has the potential to kill.

Slips, Trips and Falls

Slips, trips and falls are the main cause of accidents in the workplace causing anything from minor bruising to fractures and serious injuries resulting in time off work.

The main causes of slips and trips are:

Wet floors.

Floors or floor coverings in poor condition.

Damaged stair treads or loose stair carpets.

Inappropriate footwear.

Carrying items that obstruct the person's view.

Trailing electrical cables.

Blocked route ways.

Poor lighting.

Controls include:

Mop spills immediately and dry mop once floors have been wet mopped.

Good maintenance and repair.

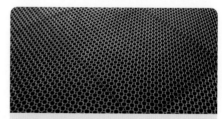

Selection of non-slip flooring and footwear.

Provide suitably located sockets to avoid trailing cables.

Good housekeeping, safe systems of work and effective supervision.

Use of safety signage, e.g. wet floor signs.

Occupational Health

Occupational health is the promotion and maintenance of physical and mental well-being of all staff. Health problems directly related to a person's job are defined as an occupational illness.

Some hazards, such as skin contact with chemicals causing short-term irritation and/or rashes are known as **acute** illnesses. **Chronic** illnesses develop gradually and their effects may be irreversible, e.g. loss of hearing. Some may even appear years after the time of employment, e.g. asbestosis.

Health Hazards

Physical damage from noise, heat and radiation, e.g. hand arm vibration syndrome by machine operators using vibrating machinery such as strimmers, soil compactors and drills.

Chemical problems from harmful dust, liquids, and/or fumes, e.g. dermatitis causing severe irritation and cracking of the skin in occupations such as cleaners or hairdressers.

Ergonomic problems from poorly designed work areas, e.g. work-related upper limb disorders, back pain or repetitive strain suffered by keyboard operators and tool operators.

Biological hazards from infectious diseases and agents, e.g. hepatitis caused by needle stick injuries to hospital staff.

Occupational health specialists may be used by employers for advice, to help assess specific risks, or to monitor the health of employees. Medical screening by an occupational health practitioner may be carried out where a particular hazard has been identified, e.g. in a workplace with high levels of dust, workers may have their lung function tested periodically.

As well as specific health hazards there are some general things that may affect all workplaces:

Smoking

Smoking and passive smoking have been linked to lung cancer, irritation to the respiratory system and other harmful effects.

The Smoke-free *(Premises and Enforcement)* Regulations 2006 bans smoking in all workplaces where more than one person is employed and places open to the public that are enclosed or substantially enclosed. This includes temporary structures such as tents/awnings. A substantially enclosed place is a structure with a roof that has walls covering 50% or more of the wall area *(including doors and windows)*.

The law also applies to vehicles if used by the public or used at work other than a domestic car. There may be other areas such as petrol stations where smoking is banned for safety reasons.

Alcohol

Alcohol increases the time it takes to react to situations, affects behaviour and reduces performance.

Drugs

Substance abuse may cause health problems and can cause safety hazards in the workplace. Many drugs are particularly dangerous because they cause mood changes and alter people's perceptions. Even prescribed drugs may have a detrimental effect. As with alcohol, the condition must be addressed.

Violence

Verbal abuse, threats, bullying or assault can cause stress and concern as well as physical injury.

Staff should be encouraged to report all occurrences to their supervisors who should record and investigate the details and if necessary report to the relevant authority.

Stress

A large percentage of sick leave is due to stress, either due to 'personal' reasons or the physical or emotional pressure of the job. Stomach and skin conditions, heart disease and depression have been linked to stress.

Factors influencing stress in the workplace include poor working conditions, overwork, job insecurity, peer pressure including harassment, unrealistic targets and poor management.

Employees should be encouraged to report stress and management should be trained to recognise the symptoms and causes of stress such as inability or reduced ability to cope with normal tasks and situations, increased sick leave and/or poor time-keeping.

Occupational health is good for you, good for your colleagues and good for your employer.

Health, Safety and Welfare in the Workplace

The Workplace *(Health, Safety and Welfare)* Regulations 1992 state that employers have a duty to provide basic facilities, such as toilets, drinking water and washing facilities, to make the workplace environment safe and healthy. The workplace may be defined as 'any premises or part of premises made available as a place of work'.

These regulations do not apply to domestic premises and exclude homeworkers. Things that should be considered to make sure a workplace is as safe and healthy as possible are covered in this section.

Structure and Design

Buildings must be solid and made from materials that meet legal requirements *(i.e. no asbestos)* and appropriate to the work activity *(so not a timber hut for welding because of the obvious fire risk)*. The internal layout should take account of the work activities to enable people to do their jobs safely. Careful planning in design can do much to prevent future accidents from people working in cramped or unsafe conditions.

Construction sites where building work is taking place also create hazardous environments that need special consideration.

Lighting

Adequate lighting must be provided in all workplaces, where possible by means of natural light. Emergency lighting must be provided in situations when failure of the main lighting systems creates a danger.

Staff Training and Supervision

Employers are required to make sure all employees are competent to carry out their role safely. This should include informing the employee of any health and safety implications when they start a new job or change their role. Supervisors should make sure safe working procedures are understood and followed. Ongoing training should also be arranged to reduce the risk of accidents.

Housekeeping

The workplace, furniture and fittings should be kept clean and tidy and all equipment stored in the proper place. All waste products and packaging should be disposed of so they don't present a hazard, obstruction or means by which fire can spread.

Workstations and Seating

People should have adequate space to work in since overcrowding can lead to stress and working in confined spaces while using tools or manual handling can lead to accidents. People should be able to leave the workstation quickly in an emergency. If possible, work should be conducted sitting down and if necessary a footrest must be provided.

Floors, Stairways and Traffic Ways

Anywhere that people move should be maintained in good repair and regularly monitored to make sure it is free from obstructions of any sort. Uneven floors can lead to slips, trips and falls; the most common types of workplace accidents.

Carpets should be regularly checked to ensure close fitting. All stairways should be fitted with handrails and open stairways fitted with guard-rails.

Maintenance

Buildings, equipment and safety devices should be checked regularly. A routine maintenance programme, procedures for reporting faults and making sure repairs are carried out promptly by a qualified person will improve workplace safety.

Temperature and Ventilation

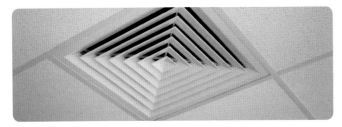

A reasonable temperature must be maintained; 16°C is considered reasonable for sedentary work *(low physical activity)*; 13°C for strenuous physical work. Any means of heating or cooling provided must not give off any noxious fumes. Enclosed workplaces must be well ventilated, where possible by fresh air. If mechanical ventilation is necessary it must be fitted with appropriate alarms to warn of failure. There is no upper temperature limit but risk assessments should be done if temperatures are excessive.

Doors, Gates, Lifts and Escalators

These must be fitted with appropriate safety devices.

Glazed Structures, Windows and Skylights

Where there is a risk of contact and subsequent breakage of the glazed areas, the glazing should be made of a safety material or otherwise protected against breakage and be clearly marked to show its presence. Where windows and skylights are able to be opened, closed, adjusted and cleaned they must be able to do so without creating any risks to the operator.

Toilets, Rest and Washing Facilities

Men and women should have separate toilet facilities unless each toilet is in a separate room with a lockable door. Toilets should be kept clean and well maintained. The needs of the disabled must also be considered. In addition, drinking water must be provided, together with hand washing facilities with hot and cold running water. In some occupations, areas must be provided for resting, eating and changing.

Unless the approved leaflet version is given to all employees, it is a legal requirement for all businesses to prominently display this poster.

Safety Signs

To make sure employees, visitors and contractors are aware of health and safety issues, employers are required to clearly display relevant health and safety information. The colour and shape of safety signs are also specified in law. They are as follows:

Prohibition:
Red border and crossbar from top left to bottom right, on a white background.
E.g. No smoking.

Mandatory:
Must Do! Circular in shape with a white symbol on a blue background.
E.g. Wear ear protection.

Safe condition:
Square or rectangular in shape, with a white symbol on a green background.
E.g. First aid equipment.

Warning:
Yellow triangle with a black border.
E.g. Slippery floor.

Information:
Square or rectangular in shape, with a white symbol on a red background.
E.g. Fire extinguisher.

A safe workplace is **everyone's** responsibility.

First Aid in the Workplace

Employer's Responsibilities

Under Health and Safety law, an employer has a responsibility to make sure the first aid provision in the workplace is sufficient. This includes:

- Carrying out an assessment to decide where, how many and what type of first aiders are needed
- Providing training and refresher training for their first aiders
- Providing sufficient first aid kits and equipment for the workplace
- Making sure all staff are aware of how and where to get first aid treatment

First Aid Needs Assessment

All employers must carry out a first aid needs assessment that should consider:

- The nature of the work and workplace hazards and risks
- The size of the organisation
- The nature of the workforce
- The organisation's history of accidents and illness
- The needs of travelling, remote and lone workers
- Work patterns such as shift work
- The distribution of the workforce
- The remoteness of the site from emergency medical services
- Employees working on shared or multi-occupied sites
- Annual leave and other absences of first aiders
- First aid provision for non-employees

Considering the nature of the work and workplace hazards and risks is one of the more complicated areas of the first aid needs assessment. The following table, compiled using information from the HSE, identifies some common workplace risks and the possible injuries that could occur:

Risk:	Possible injuries requiring first aid:
Manual handling	Fractures, lacerations, sprains and strains.
Slip and trip hazards	Fractures, sprains and strains and lacerations.
Machinery	Crush injuries, amputations, fractures, lacerations and eye injuries.
Working at height	Head injury, loss of consciousness, spinal injury, fractures, sprains and strains.
Chemicals	Poisoning, loss of consciousness, burns and eye injuries.
Electricity	Electric shock and burns.
Workplace transport	Crush injuries, fractures, sprains and strains and spinal injuries.

First Aiders and Appointed Persons

There are two levels of HSE recommended first aid courses – **First Aid at Work and Emergency First Aid at Work**.

HSE guidance states employers 'should ensure' first aiders 'remain competent to perform their role'. The guidance recommends that first aiders attend **annual refresher training**, which fulfils this requirement.

Annual refreshers are recommended due to the wealth of evidence on the severity of 'first aid skill fade'. The flow chart to the right shows the HSE's recommended sequence of training.

Although rare, if a first aid needs assessment identifies that first aiders are not needed, the minimum requirement is to appoint a person to take charge of first aid arrangements at work. The role of an 'appointed person' includes calling the emergency services if required and looking after first aid equipment.

An 'appointed person' is not a qualified first aider.

An employer should consider the risks and identify what possible injuries could occur in order to ensure sufficient first aid provision is available and first aiders are trained to the correct level.

Content of HSE Recommended First Aid Courses

EFAW = Emergency First Aid at Work (1 day course) FAW = First Aid at Work (3 day course) REQ = First Aid at Work Requalification (2 day course) AR = Annual First Aid Refresher (3 hour course)	EFAW 1 day (6 hours)	FAW 3 day (18 hours)	REQ 2 day (12 hours)	AR (3 hours)
Acting safely, promptly and effectively in an emergency	•	•	•	•
Cardiopulmonary Resuscitation (CPR)	•	•	•	•
Treating an unconscious casualty (including seizure)	•	•	•	•
Wounds and bleeding	•	•	•	•
Shock	•	•	•	•
Minor injuries	•	•	•	
Choking	•	•	•	
Preventing cross infection, recording incidents and actions and the use of available equipment	•	•	•	
Fractures		•	•	
Sprains and strains		•	•	
Spinal injuries		•	•	
Chest injuries		•	•	
Severe burns and scalds		•	•	
Eye injuries		•	•	
Poisoning		•	•	
Anaphylaxis		•	•	
Heart attack		•	•	
Stroke		•	•	
Epilepsy		•	•	
Asthma		•	•	
Diabetes		•	•	

IMPORTANT:
These topics are not covered in the Emergency First Aid at Work course syllabus.

NOTE: First aiders should be trained to deal with the possible injuries or illness identified in the first aid needs assessment; so if the need for First Aid at Work (3 day) training is identified, it is not acceptable to provide Emergency First Aiders.

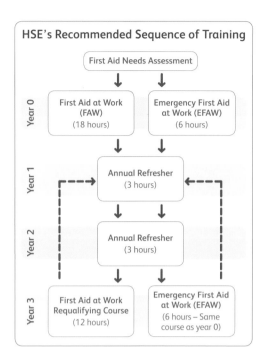

HSE's Recommended Sequence of Training

First Aid Kits and Equipment

First aid kits should be identified by a white cross on a green background. Most workplace first aid kits conform to British Standard BS 8599 and are available in different sizes to suit the environment. If there is no mains tap water, have at least 1 litre of sterile water available for eye-washing. Tablets and medicines should not be stored in a first aid kit because first aiders are not trained to administer or dispense them.

Recommended size of kit:	Small	Medium	Large	Travel	Personal	Critical injury
Lower Risk: e.g. Offices, shops and libraries etc.	Less than 25 employees	25 – 100 employees	More than 100 employees	For travel and motoring	For personal issue	For catastrophic bleeding control
Higher Risk: e.g. Food processing, assembly work, warehousing, engineering, construction, manufacturing etc.	Less than 5 employees	5 – 25 employees	More than 25 employees			

Contents:	Small	Medium	Large	Travel	Personal	Critical injury
Bandage, conforming	1	2	2	-	-	-
Bandage, triangular	2	3	4	1	1	-
Dressing pad, adhesive	-	-	-	1	-	-
Dressing, burn	1	2	2	2	-	-
Dressing, eye pad	2	3	4	-	-	-
Dressing, finger	2	3	4	-	-	-
Dressing, haemostatic	-	-	-	-	-	2
Dressing, sterile, large	2	3	4	-	1	-
Dressing, sterile, medium	2	4	6	1	-	-
Dressing, trauma, large	-	-	-	-	-	2
Dressing, trauma, medium	-	-	-	1	-	-
Foil blanket	1	2	3	1	1	1
Gloves, nitrile *(pairs)*	6	9	12	2	2	2
Guidance leaflet	1	1	1	1	1	1
Plasters, wash-proof	40	60	100	10	10	-
Resuscitation face shield	1	1	2	1	1	-
Shears *(for cutting clothing & leather)*	1	1	1	1	1	1
Tape, microporous	1	2	3	-	-	-
Tourniquet	-	-	-	-	-	1
Wipes, alcohol free	20	30	40	10	4	-

First aid is immediate treatment given to save life and stop conditions getting worse.

Equipment in the Workplace

The Provision and Use of Work Equipment Regulations 1998 specifically cover equipment, including:

Plant
Large fixed or mobile equipment such as an automatic car wash, JCB diggers or forklift trucks.

Machinery
Seemingly harmless equipment like a fax machine to meat slicers or band saws.

Tools
Simple things like a screwdriver or a sharp chopping knife.

Employers
It is the employer's responsibility to provide and maintain suitable, safe equipment. An employer is also responsible for providing training and information on risks and precautions.

Employees
It is the employee's responsibility to select the correct machine for the work to be undertaken, make sure they are trained in its use and operate the machine according to the safe working procedures laid down by the company.

The Five Main Dangers:

Traps *(Entrapment)*
Moving equipment that can trap body parts, such as presses and hydraulic jacks.

Contact
Abrasions, bruising or friction burns can occur when people accidentally come into contact with moving parts.

Impact
Moving parts may hit operators or the public if unguarded or badly sited.

Ejection
Some unguarded equipment, e.g. drills and saws, may throw off bits of metal or wood.

Entanglement
Moving machinery such as rollers, cogs and conveyors that can entangle hair, jewellery and clothes, even pulling whole bodies into machinery.

Guards and Safety Features

Guarding is often used as a method of controlling the risks associated with moving parts and machinery. Some guards act as a permanent barrier to prevent people from gaining access to a dangerous area. Other moveable types will prevent the machine from operating unless the guard is in place. It is important that guards and other safety features, such as emergency stop buttons and alarms, are working correctly – if they are not, the machinery should not be used.

Rules for Using Hand Tools:

- Select the right tool for the right job
- Make sure the tool is maintained and in good condition
- Report broken or worn tools to a supervisor
- Only use tools you have been trained to use
- Use the tools correctly
- Store correctly after use

Rules for the Safe Use of Machinery:

Guards

Never attempt to remove or defeat machine guards. Many guards operate on a 'failure to safety' system; if the guard is not in place the machine will not work, i.e. it fails to its safest condition – **OFF.**

Power

Always turn off machines and power when not in use. Turn off and unplug for cleaning or maintenance.

Lighting

Use effective lighting to enable the machine to be used safely.

Housekeeping

Keep the workplace clean. Untidy areas around machinery can cause falls and provide fuel for fires.

Repairs

Report any faults or suspected faults immediately, including missing guards or safety equipment.

Clothing

Do not wear loose clothing around machinery: no ties, belts or straps. If operating machinery avoid wearing jewellery. Wear suitable personal protective clothing or equipment if provided for the task. Keep long hair tied up or covered if using machinery.

Training

Do not use equipment unless trained to do so. Some machines may not be used by young persons *(under 18)* without supervision.

Responsibility

Wear any protective equipment deemed necessary by risk assessment. Do not 'mess about'. Never distract colleagues who are using machinery or other equipment.

Ensuring Equipment Safety

When selecting equipment it is important to choose the safest possible option for any work activity. Whether selecting or purchasing you must:

- Ask technical questions and compare the information provided by suppliers
- Check that the equipment has a CE mark
- Satisfy yourself that you have obtained all the relevant safety information
- Make sure sufficient, relevant training is given
- Undertake a risk assessment before any equipment is installed or used

Equipment must be well maintained to make sure it is in safe working order. The maintenance should be carried out according to the manufacturer's instructions by a competent person.

Equipment is only as safe as the person using it.

Tools and machines do not have feelings, they just keep going.

Personal Protective Equipment (PPE)

The final level of control in the event of an unavoidable hazard is Personal Protective Equipment *(PPE)*. It must be provided free of charge by employers.

PPE includes any equipment or clothing intended to be held or worn by people at work to offer protection against identified problems.

Where more than one item of PPE is required to be used simultaneously, e.g. hearing defenders and safety helmet, the items must be compatible and must not interfere with the level of protection offered by the individual items. Many manufacturers offer integrated systems.

PPE Rules

The item must:

- Be suitable to protect against the risk and fit properly
- Give adequate protection
- Be compatible with other equipment worn
- Carry a CE mark
- Be cleaned and maintained regularly and be replaced if worn or broken. This includes changing filters, eye shields, etc. as necessary
- Be thoroughly cleaned or washed, before removal if contaminated to avoid accidental contact by the user
- Be correctly stored in a well ventilated and clean area
- Be worn. Employers may take disciplinary action against employees who will not wear PPE

PPE must meet certain EU requirements and standards which confirm it meets specified safety and various test criteria. Generally PPE that carries the CE mark will meet these criteria.

It should always be remembered that PPE does not change the hazard in any way, it only offers protection for the wearer.

Types of Personal Protective Equipment

Protection	PPE Examples	Work Examples
Head	Helmets.	Construction, mining and other groundwork or work where there are risks of falling objects.
Face	Visors and face shields.	Welding and foundry work *(molten metal splashes)*.
Eye	Goggles and glasses.	Welding work with lasers or where there is a risk of flying fragments or chemical splashes.
Ear	Plugs, muffs and helmets.	Work in noisy environments, e.g. heavy duty drilling and/or hammering.
Hand	Gloves *(rubber, chain mail)*.	Work involving the handling of hazardous substances, chainsaws, knives, saws, hot/cold items, rough wood, etc.
Respiratory system	Respiratory protective equipment *(breathing apparatus, respirators and nose/mouth masks)*.	Work in unhealthy atmospheres and/or involving exposure to hazardous substances and work producing substantial quantities of dust.
Body	Clothing *(high visibility/thermal, cut resistant, safety harnesses, etc.)*	Work involving risks of splashing or other contamination, work with chainsaws *(arms and legs)* or ionising radiation, etc. Work where there is a risk of falling.
Foot	Safety boots and gaiters *(toe protectors, insulating footwear)*.	Work where there is a risk of splashing or of falling objects and work with live electricity.

Train and instruct people how to use PPE properly.

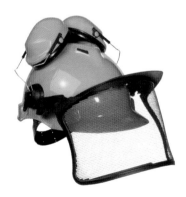

Personal Protective Equipment should only be used if the hazard cannot be controlled any other way.

Manual Handling

If a load is lifted, pushed, pulled, carried, supported or put down using physical effort it is classed as manual handling. About a third of all reported workplace accidents involve these activities and they are the most common cause of injuries resulting in more than three days off work. There is no such thing as a completely safe manual handling operation. Moving even light loads can cause injury *(either immediately or over a period of time)*. Typical manual handling injuries include:

- Abrasions, cuts and fractures
- Back pain
- Hernia
- Injuries to spinal discs and joints
- Muscle or ligament sprain or strain
- Trapped nerves

The body's ability to handle weights varies considerably in different positions. Injuries are more likely to occur when lifting loads from high or low levels, or when the arms are extended. In these positions, the weight an individual is able to handle safely is considerably less than when a load is close to their body at waist height.

> **Employers** are required by law to assess manual handling tasks with the aim of avoiding or reducing risks. Trained employees have a legal duty to follow safe working practices and use the correct techniques they have been shown.

Reducing the Risks

Where a manual handling task cannot be avoided remember **T. I. L. E.**

	You should consider:	**The risk of injury can be reduced by:**
Task	• How will the task be undertaken? • Can mechanical lifting aids be used? • Will it involve stretching, twisting or bending? • Is the task repetitive?	• Using mechanical lifting aids whenever possible • Planning a resting stage or allowing time between loads so the muscles can recover • Avoiding situations where unsafe handling techniques may be used
I **Individual**	• Who will undertake the task? • What is their ability? • Have they received appropriate training? • Do they have PPE such as gloves or safety boots if necessary?	• Attempting only to move loads that are within the physical capability of the individual *(especially if they are pregnant, have a health problem, injury or disability)* • Using more than one person if the load is too heavy or large • Making sure the correct clothing is worn *(not too tight, with appropriate footwear)*
Load	• How heavy is it? • What size and shape is it? • Where is its centre of gravity? • Could the load shift during the move?	• Reducing the load by breaking it down into smaller components • Making loads easier to hold by adding handles, insulating hot containers or wearing gloves • Not allowing the load to obstruct your view • Removing any unnecessary packaging
Environment	• Where will the task take place? • Are there any obstacles or hazards? • Can the layout, lighting or flooring be made safer?	• Checking the route is clear and any clutter is moved • Thinking about where heavy or frequently used items are stored

Safer Handling Techniques

Where manual handling cannot be avoided, using the following techniques will make each stage of the task safer.

Plan	• Stop and think about the task • Use T.I.L.E. to assess and reduce the risks as much as possible
Position	• Get as close to the load as possible • Position your feet shoulder width apart with the leading leg slightly forward • If the load has an uneven centre of gravity, position yourself so that the heaviest side is closest to your body
Lift	• Keep your head up and your shoulders level • Bend with your knees not your back • Make sure the load is kept as close to your body as possible • Check you have a good grip using your whole hand and not just your fingertips • Use your leg muscles to smoothly bring the load to waist height
Move	• Continue to keep the load close to your body • Avoid twisting and sudden jerky movements • Make sure you can see where you are going • Keep carrying distance to a minimum
Lower	• Use the same principles used for lifting, with the movement reversed to smoothly lower the load • Take care to avoid crush injuries to fingers and toes when putting the load down

Team Handling

Remember – a load can be shared between individuals to reduce the weight. This means a load may be managed comfortably between a competent team, when it couldn't be managed by one person alone. One person should take charge – good communication will make sure all members of the team move at the same time.

Use: "Ready, steady, move."

Preventing back injuries is a lot easier than correcting them.

Principles of Safe Handling

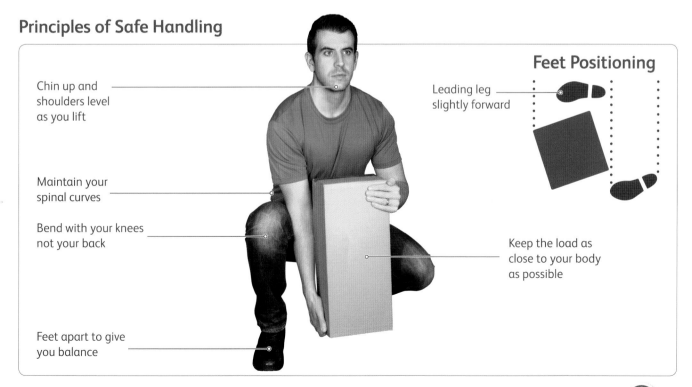

Chin up and shoulders level as you lift

Maintain your spinal curves

Bend with your knees not your back

Feet apart to give you balance

Feet Positioning

Leading leg slightly forward

Keep the load as close to your body as possible

Always assess the risks before carrying out any manual handling tasks.

Control of Substances Hazardous to Health (COSHH)

COSHH Regulations 2002 requires employers to prevent or reduce workers' exposure to substances hazardous to health.

A substance may be a:

- Powder, e.g. flour, talc, etc.
- Dust, e.g. wood, brick, coal, etc.
- Gas, e.g. chlorine, ozone, carbon monoxide, etc.
- Liquid, e.g. bleach, hydrocarbon oils, blood, etc.
- Solid, e.g. biological waste, etc.
- Biological agent, e.g. Hepatitis B, Legionella, etc.

Hazardous substances can enter the body by:

- Swallowing (ingestion)
- Breathing (inhalation)
- Contact with the skin (absorption)
- A skin puncture or cut (injection)

A COSHH assessment must consider:

- What hazardous substances are used?
- What are they used for?
- How are they used?
- What do they produce?
  (e.g. hazardous waste products)
- Who uses the substance?
- What risks are involved?
- How may an incident occur?
- How serious could the incident be – is it a major or minor health risk?

When hazardous substances are introduced:

- Obtain data sheets from the manufacturers
- Undertake and record a COSHH assessment
- Make the users aware of the danger
- Set up a training programme

In some cases health surveillance may be required to ensure the ongoing health of the workforce.

Controlling exposure:

Exposure to hazardous substances should be prevented whenever possible or safer substances substituted. Other controls that should be considered are:
- Enclose the process, e.g. fume cupboard
- Provide adequate ventilation (local extraction or general ventilation)
- Use safe systems of work to reduce the chance of spillage, leakage, etc.
- Reduce the number of people who are exposed and/or reduce the length of time people are exposed
- Provide PPE

The COSHH regulations apply to **ALL** workplaces and it is important that a COSHH risk assessment is carried out in all instances. This must be documented when there are more than five employees. **Please Note:** Data sheets are not COSHH assessments.

When handling hazardous substances:

- Make sure you read the label and follow the manufacturer's instructions
- Store them safely with lids securely fastened and away from food
- Never mix chemicals or decant them into unmarked containers
- Make sure they are clearly labelled
- Only use chemicals you have been trained and authorised to use
- Wear correct PPE and wash your hands after using chemicals

Hazard Pictograms used to Label Chemicals with their Potential Hazards:

TOXIC/VERY TOXIC

May cause destruction of living tissue or burns on contact.

GAS UNDER PRESSURE

Contains gas under pressure. Gas may be cold when released or may explode if heated.

CORROSIVE

May cause serious health risk or even death if inhaled, ingested or if it penetrates the skin.

EXPLOSIVE

May explode if in contact with flames or heat. May explode due to shock or friction.

HEALTH HAZARDS
(including carcinogens)

May cause serious long term health risks, e.g. to respiratory system. May be carcinogenic or contain highly hazardous substances that target specific organs.

OXIDISING

May cause or intensify fire.

IRRITANT/HARMFUL

May cause less serious health hazards such as skin inflammation or irritation.

HARMFUL TO THE ENVIRONMENT

Toxic to aquatic life. May cause damage to, or pollute, the environment.

FLAMMABLE

Chemicals that catch fire easily or give off highly flammable gases in contact with water.

When using any substance the most important rule is:

READ THE MANUFACTURER'S INSTRUCTIONS.

Asbestos

Asbestos was extensively used as a building material in the UK from the 1950s through to the mid-1980s. It was used for a variety of purposes and was ideal for fireproofing and insulation. Any building built before 2000 *(houses, factories, offices, schools, hospitals, etc.)* can contain asbestos.

Asbestos is the greatest single work-related cause of death from ill health. Past exposure is now responsible for thousands of people dying from asbestos related cancers every year. This is expected to increase because it can take 15–60 years for the disease to develop and there is no cure.

How is asbestos dangerous?

When materials containing asbestos are disturbed, damaged or allowed to deteriorate, asbestos fibres can be released into the air. Asbestos fibres are potentially fatal if they are breathed in. The fibres can enter the lungs and damage them causing scars that stop the lungs working properly or even causing cancer.

Who is likely to be exposed to asbestos fibres?

Anyone who disturbs asbestos-containing materials, for example, by working on them or near them. Those most at risk are those who carry out building maintenance and refurbishment work, e.g. electricians, joiners and heating engineers.

What does the law require?

Duty holders need to manage the risk from asbestos and make sure an assessment is made as to whether asbestos is, or may be present, in the building. This includes where the asbestos is, or is assumed to be and what condition it is in. It should always be assumed that asbestos could be present until a full survey is done.

A suitable and sufficient risk assessment should be made before carrying out any work that may expose employees to asbestos.

Ergonomics

Ergonomics is the science of fitting the task to the person by designing equipment and apparatus that fits well with the human body and the way that it moves. People come in all shapes and sizes so when possible work stations should be designed with adjustable features, such as adjustable seats and work platforms, so employees can work comfortably. Failure to do so can result in people stooping, stretching, overreaching and twisting. This can cause muscle fatigue, strain and possibly longer term damage or deformation.

Other factors that should be considered when risk assessing the ergonomics of work activities are:

- The degree of force that is needed to do the job
- The environmental conditions – lighting and temperature
- Adequacy of rest periods
- The repetitiveness of the task

Any machine expected to carry out repetitive motions should be regularly maintained and parts replaced as they wear out. Failure to maintain machinery may result in breakdown. People may also be expected to carry out similar repetitive tasks and suffer wear and tear as a result, causing them to suffer permanent damage and being unable to work. Any activity involving high numbers of repetitions should be looked at carefully and redesigned to avoid this as far as possible.

Occupations commonly associated with musculoskeletal problems are computer users, checkout operators, dentists and workers on production lines.

Remedies

- Alternating tasks and work breaks to avoid repetitive strain injuries
- Providing comfortable working temperatures and adequate ventilation
- Providing sufficient lighting and minimizing glare by glazing windows or supplying blinds
- Minimising vibration
- Mechanising the task
- Regular health tests may be necessary and should be promoted by employers
- Training will also help employees to be more aware of good practice

Display Screen Equipment

Display screens cause many instances of eye-strain, wrist strain, back problems and headaches. Many of these problems can be addressed by the general remedies listed above plus providing:

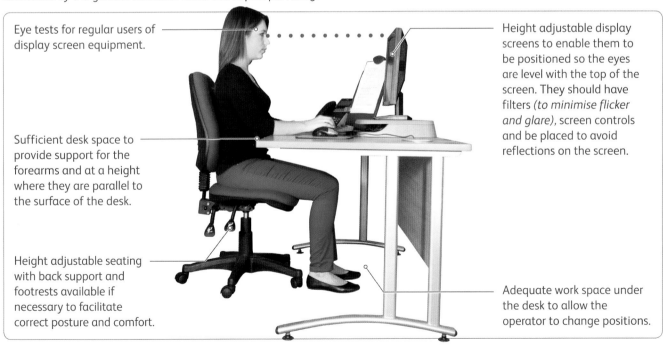

Eye tests for regular users of display screen equipment.

Sufficient desk space to provide support for the forearms and at a height where they are parallel to the surface of the desk.

Height adjustable seating with back support and footrests available if necessary to facilitate correct posture and comfort.

Height adjustable display screens to enable them to be positioned so the eyes are level with the top of the screen. They should have filters *(to minimise flicker and glare)*, screen controls and be placed to avoid reflections on the screen.

Adequate work space under the desk to allow the operator to change positions.

Staff experiencing aches and pains should report them to their employer as soon as they become aware of them.

Noise and Vibration

Any sound around us that we do not want or do not like may be defined as NOISE. While low levels of noise in the workplace are unlikely to cause harm, louder levels of noise can result in permanent hearing damage or loss.

The effects of very loud noises are often instantly apparent, but damage caused through exposure to lower levels of sound over a longer period of time may initially go unnoticed.

Noise is unwanted sound.

Symptoms of hearing damage:

- Temporary hearing loss after exposure to loud noise
- Ringing or noises in the ears *(tinnitus)*
- Difficulty in distinguishing similar sounding words
- Muffled sounds
- Background noises making conversation confusing
- Having to ask people to speak louder or increase the volume on TVs and radios

NOTE: Noise is measured in decibels *(shown as dB.)* Environments of 80dB or more require the employer to carry out a noise risk assessment and control methods should be introduced when they are required. If noise levels are above 85dB, hearing protection zones should be established and PPE provided to anyone needing to enter a hearing protection zone.

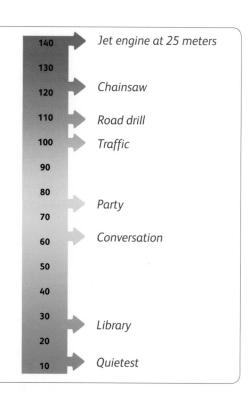

dB	
140	Jet engine at 25 meters
130	
120	Chainsaw
110	Road drill
100	Traffic
90	
80	
70	Party
60	Conversation
50	
40	
30	Library
20	
10	Quietest

Levels of control:

1. Identify the hazard and assess the risk. This requires a specialist assessment using a noise meter.

2. Reduce the noise by:
   - designing systems with low levels of noise
   - choosing machines with lower levels of noise
   - enclosing equipment in sound proofing material
   - lagging noisy ducting and pipes
   - adding acoustic dampening panels on walls and ceilings
   - having equipment properly and regularly maintained

3. Reduce exposure to personnel; can the job be done further away from the noise source?

4. Reduce the time the employee is exposed to noise.

5. Mark areas where there is a noise hazard as designated areas for protection.

6. As a last resort, if noise is unavoidable, provide Personal Protective Equipment (PPE) and proper training in its use.

When selecting PPE it is important to make sure the equipment is:

- selected carefully with sufficient rating for the noise hazard
- fitted correctly
- compatible with other PPE used by the workforce
- properly maintained
- worn whenever it is appropriate

In noise control areas, fire alarms must be supplemented with flashing lights or beacons. In the interests of safety, the wearing of hearing defenders outside the restricted area should be discouraged to make sure employees are aware of sounds around them.

Vibration

Vibration is the transmission of force from work processes into the worker. People in the course of their work may be exposed to many sources of vibration. About two million workers are at risk.

Some vibration affects the whole body, e.g. when driving a dumper truck over rough and uneven ground. Here the vibration, in the form of large shocks or jolts, is transmitted to the whole body via their feet or the seat. This could cause injury to the lower back and spine.

The most common problem is Hand Arm Vibration (HAV), which is caused by exposure to vibration, e.g. from using hand held power tools. This can be very disabling, causing severe pain in hands and arms and lack of hand movement and feeling in the fingers. It is preventable but permanent once the damage is done.

The most common problem is Hand Arm Vibration *(HAV)*, which is caused by exposure to vibration.

HAV symptoms to look for are:

- Tingling in the fingers
- Loss of feeling and sensation in the fingers
- Reduced strength in the hands
- Fingers that go white in the cold and then red and painful on recovery *(vibration white finger)*

HAV controls include:

The risks from vibrating tools or machines can be minimised by:
- Introducing methods that eliminate, substitute or reduce the exposure to vibration
- Avoiding prolonged or frequent use of vibrating equipment
- Keeping cutting tools sharp so they remain efficient
- Making sure equipment is well maintained *(wear and tear can increase vibration)*
- Avoiding forcing or gripping the tool more than is necessary
- Wearing gloves to protect the hands
- Exercising and massaging the fingers during breaks to restore circulation

Health surveillance is crucial to spot and respond to early signs of damage.

Reduce noise levels as much as possible and keep people and unwanted sounds apart.

Workplace Transport and Vehicles

Imagine a busy factory site with lorries being loaded for despatch, forklift trucks whizzing around the site, staff arriving for work in cars, visitors and staff walking around the site and delivery vehicles reversing into dock loading bays. Without controls there is every likelihood of an accident occurring. Indeed every year a significant number of people are killed in vehicle accidents at the workplace.

A risk assessment must be carried out to identify the hazards and implement controls to minimise the risk. Such controls may include:

- Clearly marking segregated traffic routes separating pedestrians from vehicles, ideally with physical barriers
- Making sure route ways are sufficiently wide for the vehicle, for example aisles between warehouse racking should be wide enough for a forklift truck to move easily and manoeuvre with loads
- Avoidance of obstructions in traffic routes by enforcing good housekeeping
- Sufficient lighting, both internally and externally, to enable drivers to identify obstructions, other vehicles and pedestrians
- Keeping traffic routes in good repair so uneven surfaces, holes, etc. do not cause vehicle damage or accidents
- Speed limits that are displayed and enforced as well as signage to alert drivers to other hazards such as low headroom, or overhead cables
- Designing traffic routes to avoid blind bends and where visibility is restricted consider mirrors or implementing a one-way system

One of the most common vehicles used in the workplace is a forklift truck and they account for many of all workplace transport accidents.

Common causes of accidents are:

- Driving too fast   • Unbalanced loads   • Horseplay

There are many different types of truck depending on the task. It is important the correct vehicle is selected for the appropriate task and that the vehicle is safe to use. As well as regular routine maintenance there are some basic start of day checks the driver should make. These include:

- Horn   • Brakes   • Oil spillages
- Lights   • Tyres   • Seat and seat belt, signs of damage

Whichever vehicle is being driven, the driver *(including agency or temporary staff)* must be trained and competent. Safe systems of work should be in place to make sure unauthorised staff cannot operate vehicles and there are sufficient breaks to stop drivers becoming overtired.

Another frequent cause of accidents is reversing vehicles. Consideration should be given to ensure adequate space for reversing vehicles and restricting access to the reversing area, which should be clearly marked and signed.

Visiting drivers should be made aware of the site layout and transport routes. It may be necessary to provide instructions in other languages for foreign drivers and allow for the fact they may have different visibility from left hand drive vehicles.

The main causes of injury involving workplace transport are people falling off vehicles or being hit or crushed by them.

Keep vehicles and people apart.

Working at Height

Falling from height is one of the biggest causes of death in the workplace and one of the main causes of major injury. Such injuries do not necessarily involve falls from very high scaffolding. They can be caused by any fall above or even below ground level such as an access ladder to an inspection chamber or sewer.

Hazards

The most common hazards include:

- Using stepladders or unsuitable alternatives such as chairs or climbing on racking
- Working on scaffolding and other access equipment with inadequate fall arrest controls
- Falling through fragile roofs or skylights
- Objects such as tools falling from height and injuring those below

Why accidents occur:

- People taking shortcuts and not using the correct equipment
- Equipment is not available or in poor repair
- Complacency, perhaps over-familiarity with the job
- Lack of awareness of the risks of working at height
- Inadequate training and supervision

Managing and selecting equipment for working at height

There are a few simple steps:

- Carry out a risk assessment of tasks that are at height. Include in the risk assessment any fragile surfaces that might break if someone worked on it or fell onto it, e.g. fibre and asbestos cement roof sheets and skylights
- If at all possible, avoid working at height and consider if the task can be done in another way, for example using a sponge on an extendable pole to clean windows instead of climbing a ladder
- If working at height cannot be avoided, use equipment or other measures to prevent falls, e.g. guard rails, work platforms, podium steps, tower scaffolds, cherry pickers or scissor lifts
- When the risk of a fall cannot be eliminated use equipment or other measures to minimise the distance and consequences of a fall, e.g. harnesses, netting and airbags
- Avoid working on, near, or passing across, fragile surfaces, e.g. repair skylights from underneath or provide fixed walkways with guard rails

Additional measures to reduce the risk of a fall when using equipment for working at height include making sure:

- The people have been trained to use it safely
- It is well maintained and regularly inspected
- There is adequate supervision to ensure people are working safely

Ladders

Ladders may be suitable for light tasks of short duration *(less than 30 minutes)*, but first consider suitable alternative methods or equipment. If ladders have been selected there are a few basic points to remember:

- Always check ladders for damage before use
- Set them at the correct angle – about 75° or the 1 in 4 rule i.e. 1 unit out for every 4 units up. If they are at too steep an angle, the ladder could topple backwards and if too shallow an angle, it may slide down the wall
- Secure it! Make sure the ground is firm, level and not slippery. Do not lean the top of a ladder against plastic guttering. Instead find a firm and resistant resting point
- Always grip the ladder and face the rungs when climbing. Try to avoid holding items when climbing but if you do need to carry something have one hand free to grip the ladder
- Do not overreach. Keep your belt buckle *(navel)* within the stiles
- Keep both feet on the same rung throughout the task and don't use the top 3 rungs of the ladder as this provides a handhold

⚠ Always maintain three points of contact with hands and feet when using a ladder.

Confined Spaces

Any significantly enclosed space where there is a risk of death or serious injury from hazardous substances, lack of oxygen or other dangerous conditions is classed as a confined space. Confined spaces with small openings such as silos, drains, sewers and storage tanks are fairly obvious, but others *(e.g. ductwork, vats, open-topped chambers)* may be less so. Before work is carried out in a confined space the hazards present must be identified and the risks assessed. This information should then be used to determine what precautions are needed and safety procedures developed *(including emergency rescue)*.

Pressure and Gas

Gas safety

Gas from a mains supply is very dangerous and can explode if not used correctly. Poorly maintained systems can cause death from carbon monoxide poisoning. It is important to make sure anyone employed to work on gas appliances is a Gas Safe registered engineer and competent in that area of gas work. They will carry an ID card specifying the appliances that they are qualified to work on.

Pressure systems

A pressure vessel is a container that holds a liquid or gas under pressure. A pressure system is one or more such vessels including associated pipework. Examples of pressure systems include compressed air systems, boilers, steam heating systems and autoclaves. If a pressure system fails during operation it can kill or injure people in the area as well as seriously damaging property by impact from the blast, debris from the explosion and fire from escaping flammable gases or liquids.

Controls include:

- Regular maintenance and correct repair from a competent person
- Safe systems of work
- Training and supervision

Gas cylinders

Gas cylinders can cause the same injuries as pressure vessels should the cylinder fail or be damaged. In addition, they can cause manual handling injuries from lifting and carrying heavy cylinders and crush injuries should cylinders fall.

Basic handling precautions include:

- Securing cylinders upright so they do not fall
- Keeping cylinders away from fire
- Making sure cylinders are not dropped or banged
- Moving larger cylinders with a special hand truck rather than dragging or rolling them
- Always checking the identity of the gas before using it

It is important to make sure anyone employed to work on gas appliances is a Gas Safe registered engineer.

If a pressure system fails during operation it can kill or injure people in the area.

Notes

Test Your Knowledge

1. **Which factors contribute to the health and safety of an office worker?** *(Page 18–19)*

A. Word processor, fan heater, comfortable temperature.

B. Good ventilation, suitable lighting, word processor.

C. Suitable lighting, good ventilation, fan heater.

D. Suitable lighting, good ventilation, comfortable temperature.

2. **Which of the following is a human factor affecting safety?** *(Page 6)*

A. Poor lighting.

B. Tiredness.

C. Poor ventilation.

D. Excessive temperatures.

3. **Which of the following is an element of the fire triangle?** *(Page 10)*

A. Water.

B. Carbon dioxide.

C. Oxygen.

D. Foam.

4. **Who enforces Health and Safety Law?** *(Page 5)*

A. The manager.

B. The HSE and EHO.

C. The police.

D. Everyone.

5. **What sort of safety sign has a white symbol on a green background?** *(Page 19)*

A. Mandatory.

B. Prohibition.

C. Warning.

D. Safe condition.

6. **An accident is:** *(Page 6)*

A. Unavoidable.

B. To be ignored if no one is hurt.

C. An unplanned and uncontrolled event.

D. Illegal.

7. **The number and type of first aiders in a workplace should be based on:** *(Page 20)*

A. The cost of the training.

B. The profits of the company.

C. The number of staff.

D. A first aid needs assessment.

8. **What is the purpose of first aid?** *(Page 21)*

A. To save life and stop injuries getting worse.

B. To educate employees.

C. To ensure complete recovery.

D. To test the first aider.

9. **Which of the following is an occupation matched with a relevant health problem?** *(Page 17)*

A. Builder – Acne.

B. Computer operator – Eyestrain.

C. Chef – Athletes foot.

D. Taxi driver – Insanity.

10. **You are asked to use a new chemical, what should you do?** *(Page 28)*

A. Read and follow the manufacturers' instructions.

B. Use it like a chemical you have used before.

C. Ask a friend what to do.

D. Refuse to use it.

11. **What is the definition of noise?** *(Page 32)*

A. Loud music.

B. Any sound.

C. A constant sound.

D. An unwanted sound.

12. **What is the best definition of a risk assessment?** *(Page 8)*

A. Stop doing things that are dangerous.

B. Identifying hazards, quantifying the risks and introducing control measures.

C. Safety instructions for a piece of machinery.

D. Looking around for problems.

13. **When lifting a box of paper you should:** *(Page 27)*

A. Maintain your spinal curves.

B. Stand with your feet apart.

C. Lift with your thighs.

D. All of the above.

14. **What is the best fire extinguisher for an electrical fire?** *(Page 12)*

A. Water.

B. Foam.

C. Carbon dioxide.

D. Powder.

15. Who is responsible for your health and safety at work? *(Page 4)*

A. You and your Employer.

B. The Health and Safety Commission.

C. An Environmental Health Officer.

D. The Police.

16. Why should near misses be reported? *(Page 6)*

A. To educate employees.

B. To test the first aider.

C. To ensure complete recovery.

D. To stop a more serious event occurring.

17. What is the BEST action when controlling the use of a hazardous substance? *(Page 28)*

A. Follow manufacturers' instructions.

B. Substitute with a non-hazardous alternative.

C. Wear PPE.

D. Ask someone else to do it.

18. What does the term 'failure to safety' mean? *(Page 23)*

A. The employer has not recognised their responsibility.

B. You have been negligent.

C. The machine cannot be turned off.

D. If there is a fault or a guard is opened, the machine will turn off.

19. When discovering smoke coming from under a door you must: *(Page 11)*

A. Carry on working until the alarm is raised.

B. Open the door and have a look to see how serious it is.

C. Find a manager or supervisor.

D. Raise the alarm, call the Fire Service and leave the building.

20. What should you do first if you discover someone who has suffered an electric shock? *(Page 15)*

A. Go and find a broom handle.

B. Call the electricity supply company.

C. Ensure they are isolated from the electricity supply.

D. Shake the shoulders and ask "are you all right?".

Notes

Glossary

Accident
An unplanned or unexpected event that causes damage to persons, equipment, stock, buildings etc.

Accident Book
Forms on to which details of **all** accidents may be recorded.

Acute
An effect on the body that occurs rapidly after a short exposure to a health hazard.

Breach
The infringement of a legal right or duty.

Chronic
An effect on the body that occurs after a long period of exposure or repeated exposure to a health hazard.

Combustible Materials
Any material that is able to catch fire and burn.

Competent Person
A person who has sufficient training, experience, knowledge or other relevant qualities to enable them to undertake a task/job.

Control Measure
Action or procedure put in place to reduce risk to an acceptable level.

COSHH
Control of Substances Hazardous to Health.

dB
Decibel – unit measurement of sound.

Electric Shock
An electric current that passes through the body's organs, muscles and nerves and may affect their function, e.g. stopping the heart.

Ergonomics
The application of scientific information concerning human beings and the design of objects, systems and environments for human use.

Escape Route
The designated route out of the building in the event of an emergency.

Exposure
Contact with a health hazard.

First Aid
Immediate aid given to an injured person to stop conditions getting worse until professional help arrives.

First Aider
Someone trained to a recognised standard to administer first aid.

Hazard
Something that has the potential to cause harm.

Hazardous Substance
Any gas, liquid, solid, powder, fumes or biological agent with the potential to cause illness or injury to the people who come into contact with it.

HAVS
Hand Arm Vibration Syndrome.

Hierarchy of Control
Control measures listed in order of priority.

HSE
Health and Safety Executive. Non-departmental public body responsible for workplace health, safety and welfare.

Inspection
Inspection is a visual or more rigorous check, including testing when appropriate, by a competent person.

Liability
Legal obligation or duty.

Load
An object to be moved, held or positioned.

Manual Handling
Using physical effort to lift, carry, push or pull a load.

Musculoskeletal Disorders (MSDs)
Include problems such as lower back pain, joint injuries and repetitive strain injuries of various sorts.

Noise
Unwanted sound, often loud.

Occupational Health
The promotion and maintenance of physical and mental well-being of all staff.

Personal Emergency Evacuation Plan
Plan for anyone who will need help during an evacuation.

PPE
Personal Protective Equipment. Clothes or equipment worn to protect the wearer against hazards.

Reasonably Practicable
A risk/sacrifice computation made to see what safety measures are reasonable under given circumstances of cost/benefit.

Responsible Person
The person with ultimate responsibility for safety in the workplace.

RIDDOR
Reporting of Injuries, Diseases and Dangerous Occurrences Regulations.

Risk
The likelihood of the hazard actually doing damage.

Risk Assessment
A proactive technique for preventing accidents and illness by identifying problems and introducing control measures.

Sound
Vibration in the air made by a source and received by the hearer.

Workplace
The normal premises, or part of the premises, which are not domestic premises and available to a person as a place of work.

Workstation
An assembly comprising of Display Screen Equipment (DSE) and any optional accessories i.e. telephone, modem, chair etc., and the immediate environment around the DSE.

Young Person
A person who has ceased to be a child (over school leaving age) but is not yet 18.